Visualizing and Verbalizing® Stories

N

BOOK 1

To all
the imagery
waiting
to be
awakened

Introduction

This book contains original stories and higher order thinking (HOT) questions written specifically for the *Visualizing and Verbalizing Language Comprehension and Thinking*® (V/V®) program.

High in imagery—often focusing on the imagery of color, size, and movement—the paragraphs are self-contained and assist individuals in developing an imaged gestalt. The stories are followed by detail, main idea, conclusion, inference, and prediction questions.

The stories are approximately graded from kindergarten through eighth grade, with several short paragraphs at every level and some multiple paragraphs at most levels. The quantity of the content is identified at the far right margin of each selection. Remember, the Sentence by Sentence step of V/V® should have no more than five parts (sentences) to visualize and verbalize. Thus, stories with six or more sentences may be used for the Multiple Sentence and Whole Paragraph steps, or sentences can be combined down to five sentences for the Sentence by Sentence step. Multiple paragraphs may be used for the Paragraph by Paragraph step. Though the stories are graded, *they are not meant to be used to pace individuals through the development of gestalt imagery*. Some individuals will only need to do a few low level paragraphs, while others may need to do more than is provided in this book! Here is some pacing advice.

- Most individuals, unless very young or severely impaired in language processing, should start at Level 3 (third grade). This allows them to begin the V/V® process of developing an imaged gestalt without having to cope with complex vocabulary or content.

- You are the diagnostician in deciding when to move from one V/V® step to another or from one grade level to another. Here's a tip. Notice how many questions you are having to ask to stimulate imagery. When you notice that images are being generated without the need for much questioning, it's time to move on. In general, note when you are talking less and the student is talking more!

These books have been written specifically for the V/V® program to develop comprehension and critical thinking through dual coding. As the eminent cognitive psychologist Allan Paivio said in describing his Dual Coding Theory (DCT), "Cognition is proportional to the extent that the coding mechanisms of mental representations (imagery) and language are integrated." These V/V® stories and higher order thinking (HOT) questions are a tool to integrate visualizing and verbalizing—the dual coding of imagery and language—necessary for cognition.

Aristotle said, "Man cannot think without mental imagery." Since without thinking and reasoning we are lost, it is my hope that these V/V® stories and HOT questions will assist individuals to reason and communicate better.

Nanci Bell

Thanks to Kirk Lindamood for his help in writing these stories,
Jane Miller, Erin Bell, and Alison Bell for editing, and Val Jones for editing/layout.

Ivan illustrations by Henry Santos

Remember:

- Start your questions with "What are you picturing for...?"

- Question with choice and contrast. "Did you see the girl big or little?"

- Encourage student(s) to *gesture* and *talk*.

    - Respond to the response. "If you pictured...let's see if that matches the sentence imagery."

        - You can combine sentences to whittle a story down to five sentences for the Sentence by Sentence step.

    - Help student(s) visualize new vocabulary.

    - It is okay to reread a sentence. Use the phrase, "See if you want to add or change anything."

        - Do some stories receptively (student listens) and some expressively (student reads aloud or to self).

    - Question to the gestalt.

Table of Contents

Who wants my jellyfish?

I'm not sellyfish!

-Ogden Nash

Primary Level

Primary Level

1.

three sentences

The yellow dog dug a hole. He picked up a white bone in his mouth. Then he dropped the bone into the hole.

    1. What color did you picture the dog?
    2. Why do you think the dog buried the bone?
    3. What might he do later?
    4. What is a good title for this story?

2.

three sentences

The gray squirrel ran up the tree. He went inside a hole in the tree trunk. There he ate nuts and watched the snow fall.

    1. What did you picture the squirrel going into?
    2. What did you picture the squirrel eating?
    3. How do you think the nuts got into the tree?
    4. Why do you think he put them there?
    5. What is a good title for this story?

3.
four sentences

The cat ran after the white duck. Around and around they went in the yard. Then the duck got mad and stopped. "Uh-oh!" said the cat.

1. What did you picture the cat chasing?
2. Where did you picture the cat and the duck running?
3. Why do you think the cat said, "Uh-oh!"?
4. What is a good title for this story?

4.
four sentences

The stoplight was red. The girl waited to cross the street. The light turned green. She skipped across to her grandfather.

1. What color did you picture the stoplight when the girl was waiting to cross?
2. What makes you think the girl was glad to see her grandfather?
3. What can you picture the girl and her grandfather doing next?
4. What is the main idea of this story?

Primary Level

5. four sentences

The black cat chased the little mouse in the house. The mouse ran and ran. Then it went into a small hole in the wall. The cat banged his nose on the hole and hissed!

1. Who did you picture chasing the mouse in the house?
2. Where did you picture the mouse going to get away from the cat?
3. Why do you think the cat banged its nose on the hole?
4. Why did it hiss?
5. What is a good title for this story?

6. four sentences

The girl saw a silver dime. She picked it up. She ran to the store. Finally, the pink candy was hers!

1. What did you picture the girl picking up, and what color was it?
2. Where did the girl run?
3. What did the girl do with the silver dime?
4. Why do you think the girl didn't buy the candy sooner?
5. What might you picture the girl doing next?
6. What is the main idea of this story?

7.

The red hen laid a white egg. The farmer took the egg from the nest. In the kitchen, the farmer fried the egg in a pan. He loved his hen!

      1. What color did you picture the hen that laid the white egg?
      2. Where did you picture the farmer taking the new egg?
      3. Why do you think the farmer loved his hen?
      4. What do you think the farmer did next?
      5. What would be a good title for this story?

8.

A boy was ice skating on the lake. Around and around he went. Then his foot went into a hole. Boom-di-dee-boom—down he went!

      1. What movement did you picture the boy doing?
      2. Do you think the boy might have gotten hurt when he fell? Why?
      3. What do you picture happening next to the boy?
      4. What would be a good title for this story?

Primary Level

9.

A green frog was asleep on a leaf. He woke up and saw a fly buzzing around. Out came his tongue. In went his dinner!

    1. What color did you picture the frog?
    2. What did you picture the frog sleeping on?
    3. Why do you think the frog uses his tongue to eat with...and not a fork?
    4. What do you think the frog will do next?
    5. What is the main idea of this story?

10.

The baby pulled the yellow toy duck across the floor. Quack, quack, quack it went. The baby laughed and laughed, and went faster. The duck went, quack, quack, quack, quack, quack, quack, quack, quack, quack...

    1. What color did you picture the toy duck?
    2. What did you picture the baby pulling across the floor?
    3. What did you picture the toy duck doing as the baby pulls it?
    4. Why do you think the baby pulled the toy duck faster?
    5. What would be a good title for this story?

Level One

Level One

1.

three sentences

The farmer went into the barn. The cows were waiting for him. He got a bucket and started to milk the cows.

      1. Where did you picture the farmer?
      2. Who did you picture the cows waiting for?
      3. Why do you think the cows were waiting for the farmer?
      4. What would be a good title for this story?

2.

three sentences

The little blue egg was in the nest. Soon there was a crack in the egg. A baby bird without feathers popped out of the egg: "Peep, peep."

      1. What color did you picture the little egg?
      2. Where did you picture the egg?
      3. What did you picture popping out of the egg?
      4. Why do you think the baby bird didn't have feathers when it came out?
      5. What is a good title for this story?

3.

The monkey held the green balloon by its string. Oops, he let the string go. The balloon flew up into the sky. The monkey jumped up and down!

1. What did you picture the monkey holding?
2. Why do you think the monkey jumped up and down?
3. Was he happy, sad, or mad? Why?
4. What do you picture happening next?
5. What is a good title for this story?

4.

The tree in the yard had red leaves. Soon the leaves fell to the ground. The wind blew them all around. The girl got her rake.

1. What color did you picture the leaves on the tree?
2. Why do you think the girl got her rake?
3. What do you picture the girl doing next?
4. What would be a good title for this story?

Level One

5.   four sentences

The little blue bird got to the edge of her nest. An old cat watched from below. The bird flapped her little wings. Flap, flap, flap, and away she flew!

1. What color did you picture the bird?
2. Why do you think the old cat was watching the nest?
3. Why do you think the bird flew away?
4. Do you think the blue bird was young or old? Why?
5. What would be a good title for this story?

6.   four sentences

The red kite was stuck in a tree. The tree was too tall for the two sisters to climb. They cried and cried. Then the wind blew and the kite fell down to the ground.

1. What color did you picture the kite?
2. Why do you think the girls started to cry?
3. How do you think the girls felt when the kite fell to the ground? Why?
4. What do you think the girls did with the kite next?
5. What is the main idea of this story?

7.

The girl got her red wagon. She pulled it up the hill. Then she put a big pumpkin in it. Down the hill, over the bridge, and home she went. Time to cut!

    1. What color did you picture the wagon?
    2. What did you picture the girl putting into the wagon?
    3. What do you think the girl was going to do to the pumpkin? Why?
    4. What would be a good title for this story?

8.

The red rooster began to crow. In the farmhouse, the farmer woke up. He looked out the window and saw the sun coming up. Time to get up!

    1. What color did you picture the rooster?
    2. What did you picture the farmer doing when he woke up?
    3. What time of the day do you think it might have been?
    4. Why do you think we use a clock instead of a rooster to wake up?
    5. What is the main idea of this story?

Level One

9. five sentences

It was a dark stormy night. Zap! A bright flash of lightning lit the sky. All the lights in the neighborhood went out. Dogs started barking. Then something happened that made the children cover their heads in their beds!

  1. What color did you picture the lightning?
  2. How did the neighborhood look after the lightning?
  3. Why do you think the children covered their heads?
  4. What do you think might have scared the children?
  5. What is a good title for this story?

10. four sentences

The two girls climbed up the tall tree. Up, up they went. When they got to the top, they opened up the door to their hideout. All their special stuff was waiting for them—and a skunk, too!

  1. What size tree did you picture the girls climbing?
  2. Why do you think the girls had a hideout so high in the tree?
  3. What do you think their special stuff might be?
  4. Do you think the girls were happy to see the skunk? Why?
  5. What do you think might happen next?
  6. What is the main idea of this story?

11.

The black and white cow wore a collar with a big bell. The bell rang when she walked. The farmer heard the bell and saw the cow coming down the hill toward the red barn. Time to eat!

     1. What color did you picture the cow?
     2. What color did you picture the barn?
     3. Why do you think the farmer put a bell on his cow?
     4. Who do you think was going to eat, the farmer or the cow? Why?
     5. What is a good title for this story?

12.

It snowed and snowed, and no one could go outside to play. When it stopped, the children went to the park. They made a snowman with three big snow balls, a hat, and some rocks for eyes. Last came the orange carrot!

     1. What did you picture the park looking like after it stopped snowing?
     2. How many big snow balls made up the snowman?
     3. Where do you think the carrot was going to be put on the snowman?
     4. Why do you think they used a carrot?
     5. What is a good title for this story?

Whales have calves,

Cats have kittens,

Bears have cubs,

Bats have bittens,

Swans have cygnets,

Seals have puppies,

But guppies just have little guppies.

-Ogden Nash

Level Two

Level Two

1.

The cowboy got on the black horse. The horse started bucking and bucking. The cowboy went flying in the air.

    1. What color did you picture the horse?
    2. Why do you think the horse started bucking?
    3. What do you picture the cowboy doing next?
    4. What do you think a good title for this story might be?

2.

The circus woman got on the elephant. Around the ring they went. Then the elephant held her with his trunk. The crowd clapped and clapped.

    1. Who did you picture getting on the elephant?
    2. Why do you think the crowd clapped when the woman was on the elephant's trunk?
    3. What do you think might happen next?
    4. What is a good title for this story?

3.

The boy put a penny in the gum machine. He turned a knob. Nothing happened! He shook it. Then an orange ball of gum popped out.

     1. What color did you picture the gum ball?
     2. What color did you picture the penny?
     3. What did you picture the boy shaking, the knob he turned or the whole machine?
     4. Why do you think the boy shook the gum machine?
     5. What is the main idea of this story?

4.

The little rabbit hopped over to the bush. Where was his mother? He started to cry. Then his mother hopped out with a carrot in her mouth.

     1. Where did you picture the rabbit hopping to?
     2. Why do you think the little rabbit started to cry?
     3. Why do you think his mother had been gone?
     4. What do you think the little rabbit will do next?
     5. What is the main idea of this story?

Level Two

5. five sentences

The fishing rod began to bend. The smiling girl quickly reeled in the line. Uh-oh, there wasn't a fish on the hook. There was some long brown seaweed. "This isn't going to taste very good!" she cried.

     1. Which way did you picture the fishing rod bending, up or down? Why?
     2. What color did it say to picture the seaweed?
     3. Why do you think the girl smiled when the line bent?
     4. What do you think the girl's face looked like when she saw the seaweed?
     5. What is the main idea of this story?

6. three sentences

The line of black ants stretched from the sugar bowl to the anthill outside the house. Each ant carried a grain of sugar down the hole into the nest. For the ants, the sugar bowl was like a gold mine.

     1. What color did you picture for the ants?
     2. How did you picture the ants carrying the sugar? How did they hold it?
     3. Why do you think the story said that sugar is like a gold mine?
     4. What is a good title for this story?

7.

The boy's mother crushed the ice until it was soft like snow. She put the ice into a paper cup. She poured grape juice all over the ice to make a grape snowcone. Then the boy ate it with a spoon—and a big smile on his face.

1. What color did you picture for the crushed ice?
2. What movement did you picture his mother doing when she crushed the ice?
3. What kind of weather do you think it was? Why?
4. What color do you think the snowcone was when it was finished? Why?
5. What is a good title for this story?

8.

A van stopped at a yellow house. A tall woman jumped out and ran up the walk to the front door. In her hands, she held a cake with candles and white frosting. When the door opened, she began to sing.

1. What color did you picture the house?
2. What movement did you picture the woman doing as she went up the walk?
3. What color did you picture the cake?
4. What song do you think she probably began to sing? Why?
5. What is a good title for this story?

Level Two

9. four sentences

The girl in the yellow dress wrote a letter. She put the letter in a toy boat with a white sail. The wind blew the boat to the green island where the girl's grandfather stood waiting. The old man read the girl's letter and smiled.

     1. What color did you picture the girl's dress?
     2. How did the boat get to the island?
     3. Why do you think the grandfather was happy?
     4. How far away do you think the island was? Why?
     5. What is a good title for this story?
     6. Why is Grandfather on an island anyway?!

10. four sentences

In a box, there were many small green beads. A woman took a needle and strung the beads on a string. She undid the needle and tied knots on the ends of the string. Then she fastened it around her neck and went out dancing.

     1. What color did you picture the beads?
     2. What did the woman use to string the beads?
     3. What might have happened if the woman hadn't tied the knots in the end of the string?
     4. What do you think she made?
     5. Why do you think she might have had to make the necklace?
     6. What is a good title for this story?

11.

A white barn stood under some big green trees. Chickens went in and out of the open front doors. Suddenly, from inside the barn, came the sound of a horse crying out.

A boy and girl ran across the grass. They stopped in front of the barn and dropped their fishing poles. Then they quickly ran inside.

They looked around inside, but didn't see anything. So they started to kick around the straw on the floor. Then they saw something that looked like a rope laying by the gate to the horse's pen. The girl poked at it with a long stick and there was an angry buzzing. "Run! Run!" she screamed.

1. What color did you picture the barn?
2. Why do you think they went in the barn?
3. Why do you think the horse cried out?
4. What do you think made the buzzing sound?
5. Why do you think the girl screamed for them to run?
6. What do you think might happen next to the horse?
7. What do you think the children should do next?
8. What would be a good title for all these images?

Level Two

12.

Judy went down the hill on her skateboard. She swerved back and forth. Then she leaned back and made it go up on two wheels.

At the bottom of the hill was a big green bush. Brian yelled and jumped from behind the bush. Judy screamed and fell off the skateboard.

After her knee stopped hurting, Judy made Brian go up the hill. She put him on the skateboard and sent him down. Brian only made it halfway down before he fell.

1. What color did you picture the bush?
2. How do you picture Judy moving the skateboard before she went up on two wheels?
3. Which two wheels do you think the skateboard went up on, back or front?
4. Who do you think is the best skateboard rider, Judy or Brian? Why?
5. Do you think it might have been dangerous for Brian to scare Judy while she was skating? Why?
6. Do you think Brian will try to scare Judy again? Why?
7. What do you think would be a good title for all these images?

The firefly's flame

Is something for which science has no name

I can think of nothing eerier

Than flying around with an unidentified glow on a person's posterior

-Ogden Nash

Level Three

Level Three

1.

The clown came running into the circus ring. Uh-oh, he slipped on a banana peel! He was sitting on his bottom!
Everyone laughed!

1. What movement did you picture the clown doing as he came into the circus ring?
2. What did you picture the clown slipping on?
3. Do you think the clown meant to slip on the banana peel? Why?
4. What do you think the clown will do next?
5. What is a good title for this story?

2.

The Christmas tree was very small and pretty. But there were no presents under it. The children went to bed sad. That night when
everyone was asleep, a fat man in a red suit came with a big pack on his back. Presents at last!

1. What colors did you picture on the tree?
2. Do you think the fat man was anyone special? Why?
3. Why do you think there were no presents under the tree?
4. What do you think the fat man had in his "big pack"?
5. What do you think will happen when the children get up in the morning?
6. What is the main idea of this story?

3.

The boy put a tooth under his pillow. He closed his eyes and went to sleep. He dreamed a pretty fairy visited him in the night.
When he woke up, his tooth was gone, and he found three shiny dimes under his pillow.

1. What movement did you picture the boy doing after he got into bed?
2. What did he put under his pillow?
3. Do you think he "dreamed" the fairy visited him? Why?
4. How old do you think the boy might be? Why?
5. What do you think the boy looks like when he smiles?

4.   four sentences

The little girl got into her pretty princess dress for the costume party. She put on her fancy gold crown. When she got to the party, she saw a clown and a pirate. The pirate jumped at her and scared her!

   1. What size did you picture the girl?
   2. What color did you picture for her crown?
   3. How many people did you picture being at the party?
   4. Why do you think she was scared of the pirate, but not the clown?
   5. What do you think might happen next at the party?

5.   four sentences

A boy drew a circle on the white paper. In the circle, he put two black dots for eyes and a big red dot for a nose. Then he drew a big, red, smiling mouth and fluffy orange hair. His white paper was turning into something!

   1. What color did you picture for the paper?
   2. What two colors did you picture the boy using for the eyes and nose?
   3. What color did you picture for the hair?
   4. What do you think he drew on the paper?
   5. What do you think the boy might do next?
   6. What is the main idea of this story?

6.   four sentences

The old man held the camera. A yellow butterfly landed on a red rose. The old man took a picture. When the camera clicked, the butterfly flew away.

   1. What color did you picture for the butterfly?
   2. What color did you picture the rose?
   3. What kind of man did you picture?
   4. Why do you think the butterfly flew away?
   5. What do you think could have stopped this from happening?

Level Three

7.
four sentences

The pretty orange butterfly was sad to be caught in a glass jar. The boy took the lid off the jar. The butterfly flew away to the top of a big bush. The boy and the butterfly were both happy!

1. What color did you picture the butterfly?
2. Why was the butterfly sad?
3. What might have happened if the boy hadn't let it go?
4. Why do you think the boy was happy?
5. What do you think the boy might do next?
6. Title?

8.
five sentences

Five green apples hung from a leafy branch. A woman in blue jeans picked the apples and put them in her basket. No one would help her. In her kitchen, she sliced the apples to make a pie. Soon a wonderful smell filled the kitchen, and her children appeared at the door, smiling.

1. How many apples did you picture?
2. What color did you picture the apples?
3. Why did the kitchen smell so good?
4. Why do you think her family visited her *after* the pie was done?
5. Have you heard the story of the Little Red Hen? Hmmm. Why am I asking?
6. What is the main idea of this story?

9.
five sentences

Raindrops clung to the spider web. The yellow sun began to shine. Each drop of water sparkled like a diamond. The spider stepped carefully over the drops as he walked across his shining web. A fly was waiting for him on the other side!

1. What color did you picture the sun?
2. How did you picture the spider moving?
3. Why do you think the raindrops stuck to the spider web instead of sliding off?
4. What do you think the spider had in mind for the fly? A friendly chat?!
5. What is a good title for this story?

10.

A little green fish tried to swim through a big gold ring and got stuck. Then the fish bit a worm on a hook and got pulled out of the lake. The surprised fisherman took the gold ring and put the fish back into the water. The happy fish swam away.

    1. What color and size did you picture the fish?
    2. Where did you picture the fish living?
    3. Why do you think the fisherman kept the ring and not the fish?
    4. How smart do you think the fisherman was?
    5. Why do you think the fish was happy?
    6. What is the main idea of this story?

11.

Rain finally fell on the dry red desert. The water soaked into the ground. In a while, yellow and blue flowers were everywhere. Bees buzzed, birds sang, and life was good.

    1. What color did you picture the dry desert?
    2. What color flowers appeared?
    3. Do you think rain falls very often in the desert? Why?
    4. Why do you think the bees were buzzing and the birds singing?
    5. Why do you think the story said, "and life was good"?
    6. What is the main idea of this story?

12.

The little girl in the green sweater needed to buy a birthday present for her grandmother. She picked up her piggy bank and smashed it against the floor. Then she gathered up all the coins and ran to buy some hard candy for the present. Uh-oh, poor Granny had no teeth!

    1. What color did you picture the girl's sweater?
    2. What movement did you picture for what the girl did to her piggy bank?
    3. How big a piggy bank did you picture? Why?
    4. Why do you think the girl had to smash the piggy bank to get her money out?
    5. Do you think we should feel sorry for Granny? Why?
    6. What is a good title for this story?

The truth I do not stretch or shove

When I state that the dog is full of love.

I've also found, by actual test,

A wet dog is the lovingest.

-Ogden Nash

Level Four

Level Four

1.

The barbecue smelled heavenly. Wood smoke swirled around the man's head as he leaned in to turn the meat with a long fork. Then using a stick with a rag tied to the end, he basted the meat with barbecue sauce. A little later, he looked closely at the sizzling meat and finally smiled and yelled, "Come and get it!"

1. What size did you picture the fork, long or short?
2. Why do you think the man had a rag on the end of the stick?
3. Why do you think the man used a long fork instead of a short fork?
4. What time of day did you picture it being? Why?
5. What do you think will happen next at this party?
6. What was the main idea of this paragraph?

2.

The fat gray manatee swam slowly through the swampy water. Her wide flat tail moved lazily up and down. She stopped for a mouthful of the water plants that grew near the steep mud banks. Then, closer and closer, came the sound of a motor boat. Unconcerned, the manatee kept up her casual feeding.

1. What color did you picture the manatee?
2. From what you imagined, was the manatee's tail round or flat?
3. Why do you think the manatee moved her tail?
4. Why do you think her tail needed to be a certain shape?
5. Do you think the manatee was smart (or right) to be unconcerned about the motorboat?
6. What do you think might happen next to the manatee?
7. What is a good title for this story?

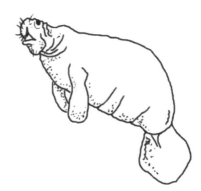

3.

The brightly colored salamander climbed slowly out of the water. He sat on a warm rock and looked around. He spied a fat pink worm wiggling around in some nearby leaves. He was about to go over and sink his sharp little teeth into it when a shadow passed over the pond. Kersplash, back in the water he went!

1. What color did you picture the worm?
2. Why do you think the salamander sat on a warm rock rather than a cold one?
3. What do you think made the rock warm?
4. Why do you think the salamander jumped back in when it saw the shadow?
5. What do you think caused the shadow?
6. What is the main idea?

4.

The mule train wound its way slowly, single file, down into the Grand Canyon. Far below, the mighty Colorado River looked like a thin brown ribbon. The steep trail was very narrow. A cliff went straight up on the left of the trail and straight down on the right of the trail. The mules didn't seem to mind, but some of the riders held onto their saddle horns very tightly. They stared straight ahead and did not look down.

1. What color did you picture the river? Green, blue, or brown?
2. Why do you think the river might be that color?
3. Why do you think the mules did not seem to mind the narrow trail?
4. What images made you think the riders might be afraid?
5. Do you think you would be more afraid riding the mules or walking? Why?
6. What would be a good title for all these images?

Level Four

5.

The girl went up the rickety stairs to the attic and came down with an old suit that smelled of moth balls. The boy found a beat-up blue felt hat in the garage. Together they stuffed the suit full of the straw. Then they drew a frowning face on a paper bag and stuffed it with straw. They put the bag on top of the suit and the hat on top of the bag, and propped the whole thing up with sticks. The new scarecrow stood guard in the garden all summer.

1. Where did the children find the suit?
2. What color did you picture for the hat?
3. Why do you think they put a frown on the face of the scarecrow rather than a smile?
4. What do you think the scarecrow was trying to keep away from the garden?
5. Do you think the face is what scares things away? Why?
6. What do you think was the result of the scarecrow standing guard?
7. What is a good title for this story?

6.

Death Valley is the lowest place in America. One spot is 282 feet below sea level. It is also the hottest area. The temperature once hit 134 degrees Fahrenheit! Death Valley was given its name when people were going to California during the Gold Rush. Many of them died from heat and thirst trying to get across it.

1. What was the highest temperature recorded in Death Valley?
2. Why do you think people continued to go through Death Valley when they were coming west to California for the Gold Rush?
3. Do you think Death Valley covers a large or small area?
4. What movement did you visualize for how people got themselves across the desert?
5. During that time, what could you do to help yourself get across Death Valley?
6. Is it different to cross Death Valley today? How?
7. What is the main idea?

Level Four

7.

The two African native trackers examined the ground. One of them noticed a bent-over weed. The other saw a scuffed place in the dirt. They looked at each other and headed off into the trees at a trot. In a while, the trackers came running back and urged the safari to hurry ahead. Later, the whole group quietly peeked through some bushes and saw the animals they had been searching for. It was a perfect photo opportunity.

1. How many trackers did you picture?
2. How do you think the bent weed helped the trackers?
3. Do you think the group was going to kill the animals? Why?
4. Judging from what you read, what kind of animals do you think the people saw?
5. What do you think the people on the safari would do next?
6. What is a good title?

8.

At the rodeo, the two cowboys pulled open the high, white, wooden gate. A huge black bull lunged out into the arena and began to buck wildly. After one really mean buck, the cowboy flew off. Uh-oh, the bull turned back to butt or trample the cowboy. The cowboy knew what the bull had in mind and tried to scramble away. Just then a rodeo clown in makeup and baggy clothes darted in and began to tease the bull. The bull chased the clown in a circle, and the cowboy quickly climbed over a fence to safety.

1. What color did you picture the bull?
2. Why do you think rodeos need clowns?
3. Do you think rodeo clowns are brave? Why?
4. Why do you think the bull chased the clown instead of the cowboy?
5. Do you think the bull caught the rodeo clown?
6. What is the main idea?

Level Four

9.

The girl got an ant farm for Christmas. It looked like a very, very thin aquarium. With it came a small container of ants, one of which was a queen. The girl went outside and filled the ant farm halfway up with dirt. Then she put the ants in the ant farm and put the ant farm on the kitchen table. Before long, the ants had dug tunnels all through the dirt. The girl and her family could now study the ants' activities with ease.

    1. How full did you picture the girl filling the ant farm with dirt?
    2. What color did you picture the ant farm?
    3. What else should the girl put in besides dirt?
    4. Why do you think an ant farm makes it easy to study what ants do?
    5. What is the main idea of this paragraph?
    6. What is a good title?

10.

Bamboo is a tall tree-like grass that is native to the tropics. The stems are hollow, woody, and jointed. Bamboo grows extremely fast: up to one foot a day. In the Far East, it is used for everything from houses to food. Peeled sprouts are cooked and eaten. Sometimes the hollow stems were used for water pipes, cut and lashed together into furniture, or made into fishing poles. There are even bamboo bridges.

    1. What did you picture the inside of a bamboo stem looking like?
    2. Do you think it is good that bamboo grows very fast? Why?
    3. Do you think it is strong or weak? Why?
    4. Would bamboo be a good plant to grow in a society? Why?
    5. What is the main idea?

11.

The fat caterpillar crawled along the limb. It stopped at every twig. Finally, it found the right one. There it stayed for awhile, getting prepared for the job ahead.

It began to spin silk around itself. The silk was shiny silver. It worked and worked, never seeming to tire. Soon it was inside its silk cocoon—its new home.

Much later, on the same twig, the cocoon began to crack. Was it the caterpillar coming back out? Yes, kind of, but it looked quite different. The caterpillar was now a bright yellow and black butterfly.

1. What colors did you picture the caterpillar silk and the butterfly?
2. How did you picture the caterpillar moving?
3. What did the caterpillar do with the silk it spun?
4. Do you think someone could see inside the cocoon? Why?
5. What do you think happened inside the cocoon?
6. Why do you think the caterpillar needed a cocoon in order to become a butterfly?
7. What is the main idea of and a good title for this story?

Level Four

12. three paragraphs

The summer sun shone down from high in the blue sky. The skin of the two boys on the blue towel began to get reddish. Suddenly, they jumped up, ran to the edge of the lake, and jumped in.

The bigger boy swam back and forth using the Australian crawl. The smaller boy waded around near the shore looking down into the water. He picked something yellow up from the bottom and yelled for the other boy to see.

After a while, the sun went behind a gray and white cloud, and the cool water began to feel colder. Still, the boys did not want to come out. Then someone yelled, "Lunch!" and out they came even faster than they went inside.

    1. What color did you picture the boys' skin after they were in the sun awhile?
    2. What color did you picture the thing that one boy found on the bottom?
    3. Do you think the boys were hungry? Why?
    4. Do you think both boys could swim? Why?
    5. What time of day do you think it was when the boys first went into the water?
    6. What do you think the boys might do after they eat lunch?
    7. What is a good title for this story?

My friends all know that I am shy,

But the chipmunk is twice as shy as I.

He moves with flickering indecision

Like stripes across the television.

He's like the shadow of a cloud,

Or Emily Dickinson read aloud.

-Ogden Nash

Level Five

Level Five

1.

four sentences

The ruby-throated hummingbird zoomed into the garden. Its wings moved so fast, they were only a blur. The little green bird flew in small circles until it spied an open flower. Then it flew over, and hovering in the air, stuck its long thin bill inside the flower to feed on the nectar.

1. What color was the hummingbird's throat?
2. Do you think the hummingbird's wings move faster than most other birds? Why?
3. Why do you think the hummingbird had to hover in the air while it got nectar?
4. How do only hummingbirds eat from the plastic feeders people put on their porches?
5. Why do you think the hummingbird had to hover in the air while it got nectar?
6. Why don't more birds eat the nectar from flowers?
7. What is a good title for this story?

2.

six sentences

Ponce de Leon struggled through the hot steamy jungle. He had sailed to the Americas to search for the legendary "Fountain of Youth." Suddenly, in a small clearing, he saw cool clear water bubbling from the ground. Ponce de Leon rushed forward, fell to the ground, and drank all the water he could hold. He believed that if he drank from the "Fountain of Youth," it would make him young again. But all that it did was make him sick with a tropical fever!

1. What color did you picture the water?
2. Why do you think Ponce de Leon was struggling through the jungle?
3. Do you think that he was thirsty? Why?
4. Do you think Ponce de Leon was egotistical? Why?
5. Why do you think the water made him sick with a tropical fever?
6. Do you think this was really the "Fountain of Youth"? Why?
7. What is the main idea of this story?

3.

The little Chihuahua dog ran to and fro on the back of the couch near the window. Its wet black nose left a long smear on the glass. The nervous little dog had barked crazily for half an hour and almost lost its voice. The cat who sat on the lawn outside the picture window was patient, as usual. Soon, hands appeared from behind and the dog disappeared. Moments later, Pee Wee found himself outside and the cat leaped happily up a tree.

1. What color did you picture the Chihuahua's nose?
2. What movement did you picture when the dog was on the back of the couch?
3. Why do you think the cat might have done this before?
4. Why do you think the cat was happy when it leaped in the tree?
5. Do you picture Pee Wee's owner happy or angry? Why?
6. Would you like to have a dog like Pee Wee? Why?
7. What is the best title for this story?

4.

The strong silver salmon was swimming upstream in the blue-black river. The big fish came to some steep, foaming, white rapids. Fast flowing water swirled around big black rocks. The salmon swam hard to get up the rapids, leaping high out of the water several times while fighting the swift current. At the top of the rapids was a clear, calm deep pool, but the salmon did not stop to rest. Instinct drove it on toward the headwaters of the river where it would lay its eggs.

1. What colors did you picture the salmon and the rocks?
2. How did you picture the salmon moving in the water?
3. Why do you think the salmon leaped out of the water when it came to the rapids?
4. Why do you think the salmon had to be strong?
5. Do you think the salmon could stop and rest? Why?
6. What is the main idea of these images?

Level Five

5.

The window rose silently and the cat burglar slipped into the room. Dressed all in black, including thin black gloves, he peered around from behind his small black mask. He tiptoed over to the bed and smiled at the sleeping couple under the blankets. Then he crossed the room to a small painting on the wall. He did not notice the small red dot that appeared for an instant on his pant leg just above the carpet. The cat burglar removed the painting, quickly cracked the safe that it concealed, and slipped back outside with the jewels in his pocket. He was very surprised, upon climbing to the ground below, to find the police waiting for him.

1. What color did you picture for the burglar's clothes and what color was the dot on his pants?
2. Why do you think the burglar wore "thin" gloves?
3. Why do you think he smiled at the sleeping people? Was he just a nice guy?
4. Why do you think this type of burglar is called a "cat" burglar?
5. Why were the police waiting for him?
6. Why didn't he hear the alarm go off in the people's house?
7. What do you think will happen next?

6.

An old farmer followed a gigantic black and white pig that was snuffling and rooting among the fallen leaves. The farmer was watching the pig very carefully. Suddenly the pig grunted with excitement and began to dig. The farmer quickly drove the pig off with a long switch and then began to dig himself. Soon he came up with a tangerine-sized black lump. He smiled, put it in a small bag, and gave the pig a treat. The pig had helped the farmer find a truffle—a rare food delicacy that he could sell for a great deal of money.

1. What is the main idea of this story?
2. What color did you picture the pig?
3. Why do you think the farmer didn't find the truffle by himself?
4. Do you think truffles could be easily grown as a farm product? Why?
5. Do you think the pig likes truffles? Why?
6. What do you think a truffle is made of? Meat? Fish? Potato? Candy? Why?
7. Title this, please!

7.

The saguaro cactus of the American southwest can reach a height of sixty feet. Its trunk can be over three feet thick. The huge cactus weighs many tons. The saguaro's skin is pleated like an accordion. When a rare rain comes, it can expand by up to twenty percent to absorb all possible moisture. The cactus can take in and store up to 100 gallons of water. This is enough to last it through the many months before the rain falls again.

1. What is the best title for this story?
2. What color did you picture for the landscape?
3. What do you picture happening to the size of the cactus as it uses up the huge amount of water it takes in when it rains?
4. If you were stranded in the desert, would you be happy to see a saguaro cactus? Why?
5. Why do you think the cactus wants to absorb all possible moisture?
6. Is a title coming to mind? Good, what is it?!

8.

A crowd began to gather in the meadow by the geyser in Yellowstone National Park in Wyoming. People came from all directions to stand behind the low log fence. There was a deep rumbling from down in the earth. Suddenly hot water and steam shot high into the air for several minutes. The crowd "oooh-ed" and "aaah-ed." They clapped when it was over and then everyone left. After an hour, more people would gather and the scene would be repeated as "Old Faithful" erupted again.

1. What could you hear in this story? What caused it?
2. Would it be good to picture a ranger? Why?
3. Why do you think there was a fence in front of the geyser?
4. From what you pictured, how often do you think the geyser erupts?
5. What is the main idea of this story?

Level Five

9.
eight sentences

A 100-foot chunk of ice broke off a glacier and fell into the sea with a huge splash. As it floated off, the iceberg only stuck up twenty feet. Most of it, eighty feet to be exact, was underwater. Several times, tired seals hauled themselves up onto the ice to bask in the sun. Passing birds would stop to rest and preen their feathers. As the iceberg drifted with the current, the water and weather got warmer. The iceberg began to melt faster and faster. Before long, the iceberg was only the size of an ice cube.

    1. How tall did you picture the iceberg when it broke off?
    2. Why do you think so much of the iceberg stayed under water?
    3. Would you be happy to drift near an iceberg if you had been at sea a long time? Why?
    4. Why did the seals and birds like to use the iceberg?
    5. What do you think would eventually happen to the whole iceberg as it went into warmer and warmer waters?
    6. What is the main idea of this story?

10.
eight sentences

It was winter on the tundra and some wolves were stalking a herd of musk oxen. The wolves had not eaten for days and their ribs were starting to show. The hungry animals were hoping for a chance to take one of the musk ox calves from the herd. A fine fat calf would make a good meal for the whole wolf pack. As the wolves crept closer, the adult musk oxen formed a circle. They stood shoulder to shoulder, facing out, sharp horns ready. Inside the circle, protected by the larger animals, the calves huddled. After some careful consideration, the wolves decided to go hunt rabbits instead.

    1. What colors did you picture the landscape and the wolves?
    2. Why do you think the wolves were skinny and hungry?
    3. Do you think they will be fatter in the summer? Why?
    4. Why did the adult oxen form a circle around the calves?
    5. Why did they face out?
    6. Do you think oxen are smart? Why?
    7. Why are the calves fat in the winter, yet other animals are hungry?
    8. Title it, please!

11.

The athletic girl climbed easily up onto the counter and opened the cupboard. She studied the brightly colored boxes inside for a long time. Finally, she hurled a red and yellow box down to the boy waiting below. Together they took bowls, spoons, and milk to the table.

They poured golden-brown cereal from the red and yellow box to fill the bowls. Then they poured the cold fresh milk on the cereal and were ready to eat. Just then a new cartoon came on the TV and they rushed over to watch. When they went back to the table, their beautiful crunchy cereal was all gray and soggy.

The two children looked at each other, made a face, and headed for the trash with their bowls. Then their mother came walking in, saw what was going on, and slowly pointed one finger. In their house, the rule was, "if you fix it, you finish it!" Back at the table, the sad pair cried and cried as they ate. It took them a while to finish the soggy cereal.

1. What is the main idea of this story?
2. What color did you picture the cereal box that the girl threw down?
3. Why did the cereal get soggy?
4. Do you think the mother was happy or angry? Why?
5. Why do you think the kids cried?
6. Why do you think it took them a while to finish their cereal?
7. What do you think happened the next time they had cereal?

Level Five

Marty's Appaloosa horse was white with small black spots. He often said it was the horse version of a Dalmatian dog. He named the Appaloosa, "Fido," many years ago, and entered Fido and himself in every parade within 100 miles.

Marty had a dirty green pickup truck that just barely ran and smoked a lot. With it, he pulled a brand new, shiny, white horse trailer that he bought especially for Fido. He kept it sparkling clean. Marty would drive, smiling, with a short cigar held in his perfect drugstore teeth that were so white they matched the trailer. Clearly, he saw nothing odd about pulling such a fine new trailer with such a sad old truck.

Sometimes people would snicker when they saw Marty's truck and trailer. But once they saw Marty and Fido in a parade, they never laughed again. Marty sat tall and proud on Fido's strong back in a shiny black saddle with lots of silver trim. He held the matching silver-studded reins in one hand, even though he didn't need to. Fido knew exactly what a parade was all about, so whenever any music began to play, Fido would proudly lift each leg as if to dance. Marty grinned and tipped his hat.

1. What color did you picture Fido?
2. Why do you think Marty named his horse Fido?
3. What color did you picture the old truck?
4. What should you picture for what the truck did when Marty drove it around town?
5. Why do you think Marty's teeth are called drugstore teeth?
6. Did it make any sense to you that Marty had white teeth and smoked a cigar? Why?
7. Do you think Fido's saddle was cheap or expensive? Why?
8. What would be a good title?

Behold the duck.

It does not cluck.

A cluck it lacks.

It quacks.

It is special fond

Of a puddle or a pond.

When it dines or sups,

It bottoms ups.

-Ogden Nash

Level Six

Level Six

1.

The giant squid floated in its silent world deep beneath the sea. Two eyes the size of dinner plates kept a sharp lookout for dinner. The squid was very hungry and was waiting to capture any prey it saw in its long strong tentacles. But wait! A sperm whale entered the picture, looking for a meal of its own. The squid, who did not wish to become that meal, released a dark cloud of ink and shot away into the gloomy distance.

    1. What movement did you picture for the squid?
    2. How big did you picture the squid's eyes, and how big would that make his body?
    3. Why do you think the squid, even though it was a giant, took off when it saw the whale?
    4. Why do you think the squid released the ink?
    5. What color did you picture the cloud of ink? Why?
    6. What do you think might happen next?
    7. What would be a good title for all these images?

2.

Florence Chadwick took off her bathrobe and shivered in the morning fog. She plunged both hands into a large bucket and then began to cover her entire body with goopy black axle grease. When she was done, she pulled on a small white bathing cap and walked into the icy cold water. Thirteen hours later, she walked out of the water on the other side of the English Channel. She had set a world record for the cold, dangerous, twenty-one mile swim.

    1. What did you picture Florence putting on her body?
    2. How many miles did she swim?
    3. Why do you think she covered her body with thick grease?
    4. What color did you picture for the bathing cap? Why?
    5. Do you think this happened recently or quite long ago? Why?
    6. Why do you think the swim was dangerous?
    7. Why do you think it was important for her to wear a bathing cap?
    8. What is the best title for all your images from this paragraph?

3.

Eskimos live on the seacoast of the far northern reaches of our planet. Since little grows where they live, they have built their lives and culture around the hunting of seals, walruses, and whales. Eskimos eat the meat and make tools, clothing, weapons, and anything else they need from all the other parts of those animals. They build circular houses called igloos out of large blocks of snow. Since snow plays a huge part in Eskimo existence, it should be no surprise that they have over thirty words for different kinds of snow.

1. What are the three animals you visualized the Eskimos hunting?
2. Did you picture bright colors in this story? Why or why not?
3. What is the main idea?
4. Why do you think the Eskimos use all parts of the animals they hunt?
5. Why do you think they use snow instead of wood to build their homes?
6. What do you think might happen to the Eskimos as more and more people move into their areas? Will it be good, bad, or both?

4.

The large black buzzard floated almost motionless in the sky. His beady, little red eyes scanned the desert floor a thousand feet below. Suddenly, the buzzard saw two dead boys lying side by side in a ravine. He circled lower and lower with the idea of having a tasty meal of rotten flesh. When the buzzard was only a few feet above the bodies, the "dead" boys jumped up, yelling. The startled buzzard let out a loud squawk and flapped away into the sky as the boys laughed and laughed.

1. What movement did you picture the buzzard doing in this story?
2. How many dead boys were there? (Watch out, this is a trick question!)
3. Why do you think the buzzard has good eyes?
4. Why do you think he thought the boys were dead?
5. Do you think the boys were smart to play this trick? Why?
6. Do you think the boys had to wait very long for a buzzard to come along? Why?
7. What do you think the buzzard might do to get even with the boys?
8. What is a good title for this story?

Level Six

5.

The ants of the world have developed some interesting ways of ensuring their food supply. Leaf Cutter ants climb a living plant and slice its green leaves into moveable sections with their scissors-like jaws. They transport the pieces to their underground nest where the pieces are chewed into a kind of mulch on which a special fungus then grows. The ants cannot digest the leaves, but the fungus can. The ants let the fungus consume the leaves and then they eat the fungus. In that way, they are able to extract nourishment from the leaves that they normally could not.

1. What colors did you picture in this story?
2. What is the name of the type of ant described in this story?
3. Do you think the leaves are soft and flexible or tough and full of fibers? Why?
4. Why do you think the ants can't digest the leaves?
5. If the ants have scissors-like jaws, why can't they digest the leaves?
6. Do you think these ants are smart?
7. How long do you think it takes the fungus to consume the leaves? Why?
8. Title, please!

6.

Archery is a sport that has individuals shoot an arrow at a target in competition. Archers stand a certain distance from a four-foot circular target. They have a bow from which they shoot a number of arrows at the target. Each tries to be the one with the most arrows nearest the center, or bull's-eye. Many people think of the bull's-eye of a target being red. But in archery it is yellow, surrounded by circular bands of red, blue, black, and then white.

1. How many feet from the target did you picture the archers standing?
2. Why do you think the bull's-eye is yellow rather than red?
3. Do you think it would be harder to hit the bull's-eye with a bullet or an arrow? Why?
4. Why do you think there are different bands of circular colors on the target?
5. Do you think each archer gets to choose the distance he or she will shoot from? Why?
6. What is the main idea of this story?

7.

Terns are Arctic birds that have two different homes over five thousand miles apart. They spend the "warm" summer months of June, July, and August nesting in large noisy colonies above the Arctic circle. When their eggs hatch, they feed their chicks by diving for fish and other sea creatures. Then, as winter approaches, the whole colony heads south, all the way to Antarctica. There it is soon "summer," and the birds stay several months. When winter in the northern hemisphere ends, they are off on the long flight north again.

1. What movement did you picture in the tern colonies?
2. How far apart are their two homes?
3. Why do you think their homes are so far apart?
4. Do you think it takes the terns a long time or a short time to get from home to home? Why?
5. What do you picture the terns doing while they are between homes?
6. Do you think the terns have many feathers or few feathers? Why?
7. What kind of birds do you picture living in the Arctic climate all year?
8. What is the main idea of this story?

8.

The very large boy told the girls that he could do any dive they named perfectly. The girls thought and thought and finally put their heads together and decided on a double flip. "Easy as pie," said the boy as he climbed onto the diving board, "Come stand right here at the side of the pool and you will see brilliant perfection." Then he slicked back his hair with his hands, ran down the board, bounced hard once on the end, and sailed high into the air. The girls screamed and tried to run, but they had seen the trick too late. He did a perfect "cannonball" and made a gigantic splash.

1. What is the main idea of this story?
2. What movement of the boy did you picture as he performed the "dive"?
3. Why do you think the girls thought up a double flip for him?
4. Do you think the boy was showing off for the girls? Why?
5. Why do you think the cannonball made such a big splash?
6. Do you think the cannonball is a real dive? Why?
7. What do you think might happen next to the girls, and what might happen to the boy?

Level Six

9.

The abominable snowman walked happily down a snowy ridge, whistling. A few large snowflakes drifted down as he moved smoothly along on his huge hairy feet. Suddenly he heard a raucous "blah, blah, blah" of a mountain climbing expedition as they clattered and chattered their way up the ridge. "Uh-oh!" The snowman turned left and moved quickly to a small snow cave and crept inside. He watched as the climbers came to his footprints and fell silent. They looked at the huge prints from his bare feet, much bigger than their own boot prints, and then hurried on up the mountain. The abominable snowman was glad they did not stop and look for him. He was a shy creature and didn't want to be found by mankind.

1. What movements did you picture the abominable snowman doing in this story?
2. What size did you picture the cave he went in to hide?
3. Why do you think the climbers hurried away when they saw the abominable snowman's prints?
4. Do you think the climbers will tell anyone that they saw the prints of the snowman? Why?
5. Why do you think the snowman didn't want to be found by people?
6. Title, please!

10.

The hurricane slowly approached the coast from far out at sea. People listened to their radios as they prepared for the storm to strike their area. Men were working fast, nailing sheets of plywood over the big plate glass windows of stores. Other people were hurriedly trying to get everything in their homes that water could damage up off the floor. The wind blew harder and harder until it reached eighty-five miles an hour, at which time all power went out. Then the wind stopped, but nobody came outside or undid any of their work. They knew the calmness was just from the "eye" of the hurricane, and soon the wind and rain would begin to howl and pound again.

1. What did you picture the men nailing over the windows?
2. Why do you think they were putting boards over the windows?
3. Why do you think people listened to their radios rather than watching TV for news of the hurricane?
4. How do you think people might get information if the electrical power goes out?
5. Why do you think the middle of the hurricane is called the "eye" of the storm?
6. What makes a hurricane so dangerous?
7. What is the main idea of this story?

11.

The gray and white cat with no tail crept through the tall green grass. The grass was very wet and when the cat shivered, little drops of water flew in all directions. The cat did not want to be in the wet grass at all, but it could not help itself. The courageous and fierce cat was born to hunt.

Right now, the cat was hunting a fat brown gopher it had spotted while sitting on the fence in the sun. It had rained for days and the cat was enjoying the sun. However, as soon as it saw the gopher, it hopped down from the fence and began to stalk. Down in the grass, the cat could not see the gopher anymore, but it could hear the little beast digging and scratching around on the other side of the yard.

Closer and closer crept the hungry gray and white hunter. If the cat had a tail, which it sadly did not, it would have been twitching with excitement as it got almost close enough to leap. Close enough now, the cat gathered its legs beneath it and sprang high in the air over a huge clump of grass, and came down on nothing! The cat looked around, completely puzzled about where the gopher could be, until it saw a smiling boy outside the yard swinging a toy gopher on a string.

1. What color did you picture the cat?
2. How do you think not having a tail might have affected the cat when hunting?
3. Do you think the cat thought what the boy did was funny?
4. What do you think will happen the next time the cat sees a "gopher"?
5. Title!

Level Six

12.

three paragraphs

At midnight the zoo was quiet. In Birdland, only the owls were awake, and a big white one let out a half-hearted hoot. A huge, dusty elephant, sleeping standing up, had a bad dream and dramatically stamped one foot on the ground. Dust and a little bit of dry yellow straw puffed up into the moonlight and then settled silently to earth.

In the guard shack by the front gate, the night watchman was watching the insides of his eyelids. Soft snoring sounds came from his nose and a thin rope of drool hung from the corner of his mouth, almost touching the badge on his shirt. Suddenly the telephone on the desk rang. Once, twice, three times it rang, but the watchman didn't move a muscle.

On the fifteenth ring the watchman finally woke up enough to flail one khaki-clad arm around in the darkness. This knocked the telephone from the desk to the floor and woke him up completely. When he finally found the receiver and put it to his ear, he was greeted with complete silence. Just as he was about to hang up, the silence was broken with a wickedly loud, "Oo-oo-oo-ee-ee-ee-aa-aa-aa." He knew what made it, but he could never prove a thing against those tricky chimpanzees, and nobody would believe him anyway.

1. What color did you picture the owl that let out a hoot?
2. What movement did you picture the elephant doing when he had a bad dream?
3. What do you think caused the yellow straw to puff up from the ground?
4. What do you think "watching the insides of his eyelids" really means?
5. What helped the watchman wake all the way up?
6. Who do you think made the phone ring?
7. Why do you think no one would believe him that the chimpanzees did it?
8. Creative title necessary!

I test my bath before I sit,

And I'm always moved to wonderment

That what chills the finger not a bit

Is so frigid upon the fundament.

–Ogden Nash

Level Seven

Level Seven

1.

In Europe, tiny crab apple fruit is pressed and made into cider. Some people even use the little apples to make jam and jellies, but crab apple trees are grown mostly to be ornamental. The fruit is usually dry, bitter, and acidic. Could that be why a crabby, mean, cranky person is sometimes referred to as "an old crab apple"?

    1. What color did you picture the little apple?
    2. What do you think might be a very important ingredient of crab jelly?
    3. Do you think the crab apple tree is attractive? Why?
    4. Why do you think it might be beautiful in spring?
    5. What is a creative title for the images in this paragraph?

2.

The albatross has the greatest wingspan of any bird—up to twelve feet across. The great seabirds are known to travel vast distances sailing high on the wind. They sleep floating on the ocean, live on squid and other marine creatures, and even drink sea water. In fact, they usually venture onto land only during the nesting season when a mated pair will incubate a single large white egg for two to three months. In the days since man has sailed the seas, the albatross has become something of a scavenger. Often they will follow ships, feeding on refuse that is thrown overboard.

    1. How large did you picture the wingspan of the albatross?
    2. How many eggs did you visualize the albatross incubating?
    3. How do you think albatrosses are able to fly great distances?
    4. Why do you think they need to drink sea water?
    5. Why do you think they like or need to follow ships at sea?
    6. Why do you think albatrosses have to nest on land? (What would you visualize the eggs doing if they were laid in the water?)
    7. What is the best title for all of your images?

3.

I watched the big fat beaver gnawing busily at the trunk of the birch tree. The tree was on the bank of a pond he had created by building a dam of small trees and other branches to block the flow of the stream. The beaver also built himself a round lodge of smaller sticks with an underwater entrance in the middle of the pond. He continued to gnaw at the birch tree and suddenly it made a loud cracking sound and fell toward the middle of the water where it landed with a great splash. As the furry little lumberjack looked at his work, I thought I heard him squeak, "TIMBER!" Was I dreaming?

> 1. What did you picture for the beaver's home in the pond?
> 2. Why do you think he built his lodge in the water with underwater entrances?
> 3. Do you think the beaver had good teeth? Why?
> 4. What do you think the beaver might do next?
> 5. What is the best title for all your images?

4.

The dark-colored tropic-dwelling frigate bird can have a ten-foot wingspan. It may float for hours, seemingly motionless, on air currents high in the sky. From this lofty viewpoint, it will then swoop down to the surface of the ocean and snatch up a fish with its strong hooked beak. If a frigate bird sees a smaller bird with a fish, it will often confront the bird in mid-air and demand the fish be given up. If the other bird refuses and tries to escape, the frigate bird will seize it from behind by the tail feathers and shake it until the fish is dropped. The frigate bird instantly releases the smaller bird and swoops down to snatch the falling fish from mid-air.

> 1. What color did you visualize the frigate bird?
> 2. Why do you think the frigate bird takes fish from other birds?
> 3. Why do you think it grabs the smaller bird by the tail feathers and not the beak?
> 4. Why do you think it gets the fish in mid-air rather than letting it hit the water?
> 5. What is the main idea of this paragraph?

Level Seven

5.

There are two kinds of camels: one-humped and two-humped. Dromedary is the name for the short-haired, tan-colored, one-humped kind. They are native to the Middle East and have been used by people there for thousands of years. Dromedaries furnish transportation as well as supplying meat, milk, hides, and wool. The two-humped Bactrian camel, also long domesticated, is found in central Asia. This camel is shorter, darker in color, and has long thick hair on its head, neck, and upper legs. The Bactrian camel has a more pleasant disposition than the Dromedary, which is known to be stubborn, cranky, and cantankerous.

1. What color did you picture the Dromedary camel?
2. How many humps did you picture on the Bactrian camel?
3. What are the many things with which the Dromedary camels furnish people?
4. Do you think people took good care of their camels? Why?
5. Which of the two camels would you rather own? Why?
6. Which camel do you think might be easier to ride? Why?
7. Title?

6.

Thousands of years ago, geese were hunted by early man, for both meat and eggs. Later, geese became domesticated and were valued for goose down, which could be plucked carefully several times a year from live geese. Goose down is still used due to its lightness, warmth, and comfort for stuffing things like jackets, quilts, and pillows. Geese have other uses also. They love grass and, if kept in a yard, will often take the place of a lawnmower. A goose will honk loudly, hiss menacingly, and sometimes even attack strangers that come on its property. Farmers like to keep geese instead of watchdogs because they are cheaper to feed and also supply the occasional egg.

1. What color did you picture for the goose down?
2. What things can you picture putting goose down in?
3. Do you think it helped or hurt the goose to have its down taken? Why?
4. Why do you think more people don't use geese instead of lawn mowers?
5. Why are geese cheaper to feed than watch dogs?
6. What is the main idea?

7.   *eight sentences*

The tomato, which originated in central America, is really a fruit; in fact, it is a berry. Taken back to Europe by explorers, tomatoes terrified the residents, who were convinced they were deadly poison. There is a story that one man put up posters advertising that he would consume a "love apple," as tomatoes were called then, that afternoon. A huge crowd gathered to watch his certain demise. The man climbed up on a stage and ate a tomato in front of the horrified crowd. Then he ate another. The crowd waited several hours for him to die a terrible death and when he did not, they all went home and began eating tomatoes. People have been eating them ever since!

    1. What was the name the Europeans gave the tomato?
    2. What is the main idea of this paragraph?
    3. What characteristics does a tomato have that make it seem like it fits in the berry family?
    4. Why do you think we often think of a tomato as a vegetable rather than a fruit?
    5. Why do you think a crowd gathered to watch the man eat the tomato, if they thought he was going to die?
    6. What do you think made the people of Europe think tomatoes were poison?
    7. What do you think happened next to the tomato?

8.   *nine sentences*

Prior to 1947, African-American athletes in America were not allowed to play professional baseball. Thanks to Jackie Robinson, who broke the color barrier, those days are gone forever. The Brooklyn Dodgers took a chance and hired Jackie Robinson to play second base for them. At first, Robinson was racially taunted by the opposing players and by unruly fans in the grandstands. He even received several death threats by mail. But Jackie Robinson wanted to play and nothing could stop him. He was such a superb athlete that he soon became a star, the insults stopped, and the way was opened for other black players. Jackie Robinson helped lead the Dodgers to the Word Series six times in his ten-year career. After he retired, he was elected to the Baseball Hall of Fame.

    1. What date did Jackie Robinson begin to play for the Dodgers?
    2. Why do you think stopping African-Americans from playing sports was called the "color barrier"?
    3. What were some of Jackie's best traits that enabled him to break the color barrier?
    4. What might have happened if Jackie Robinson hadn't come along?
    5. Main idea, please!

Level Seven

9. eight sentences

Diana Ross waited nervously behind the massive drum set and huge amplifiers at the back of the stage. A gigantic crowd had gathered to hear the star perform at a free concert in New York's Central Park. A storm threatened to spoil it all as rain fell in sheets while thunder and lightning crashed all around. The crowd, with umbrellas and jackets covering their heads, was determined to see their favorite and refused to leave. "Dia-na, Dia-na, Dia-na," rang out from the throng and Diana knew she must put aside her own fear of the storm. She signaled the band to begin to play as she strode to the front of the stage. Despite the wind and rain whipping through her hair and flattening her costume to her body, she sang with all her heart. When she was done, the crowd leapt to their feet in gratitude and love.

1. Where did you picture the concert being held?
2. Why do you think Diana Ross was reluctant to perform during the storm?
3. Do you think she is a popular singer? Why?
4. Do you think she is a caring person? Why?
5. What is the best title for this story?

10. eight sentences

Yellow Fever is a nasty disease caused by the bite of an infected mosquito. Symptoms include fever, aches, nausea, and vomiting. The sick person often becomes jaundiced, or yellow-skinned, for a time. Some victims recover and are then immune for life. In 1901, during the building of the Panama Canal, so many workers got sick that the job almost had to be given up. Then it was discovered that by controlling mosquitoes, they could control the disease. Swampy areas were drained and thin oil was floated on deeper water to kill the larvae. When insecticides were sprayed, the mosquitoes disappeared and the canal was finished.

1. What color did you visualize for the name of the disease that this story is discussing?
2. Did you visualize the four symptoms of Yellow Fever? Name them!
3. How do you think Yellow Fever got its name?
4. Why do you think they almost had to give up building the Panama Canal in 1901?
5. Why didn't they just keep getting more workers?
6. Why was it important to kill the larvae and not just spray insecticides to kill the mosquitoes?
7. Why do you think oil killed the larvae?
8. What is the best title for all these images and thoughts?

11.

The first fire trucks were no more than large wooden tubs on wheels. When a fire broke out, the firemen would wheel a tub as close as they could to a fire. There a bunch of people formed a bucket brigade to fill the tub with water. Once the tub was full, two firemen would operate a hand-powered pump while another one directed the stream of water from the pump onto the fire.

Later someone figured out how to use steam to power the water pumps. A large coal-fired boiler on a wagon was lit as soon as a fire alarm was heard. Then while the boiler built up steam, the firemen used a team of horses to pull the wagon at top speed to the fire. Once there, the firemen would immediately throw a short hose into the nearest water supply and begin squirting the water that the steam engine pumped onto the fire.

Today, most fire trucks are almost completely self-contained. A big truck's engine will power the truck to get to the fire and also run the water pump when it gets there. In addition, the engine can power one or more hydraulic ladders which can telescope to a height of about 100 feet. With these ladders, the firemen can rescue people trapped by fire in tall buildings and also spray water down onto the flames from high above.

     1. What is the main idea of all these images?
     2. What color did you picture the large wooden tubs on wheels?
     3. Do you think it took longer or shorter to put out fires long ago?
     4. Why do you think those fires often spread through blocks after blocks of houses?
     5. Do you think it was more dangerous or less dangerous to be a fireman in those days? Why?
     6. What future inventions might further improve fire fighting?
     7. Title it, please?

Level Seven

12.

three paragraphs

When the class entered the gym for Physical Education (P.E.), they found a huge trampoline in the center of the basketball court. All the boys and girls crowded excitedly around the sides of the four-foot high trampoline to listen to the coach. The coach told them the safety rules as he bounced in the center of the trampoline. Without even trying, he was flying a couple of feet into the air with each bounce.

Only two students could be bouncing on the trampoline at one time. All the others were to be positioned around the outside to catch anyone that bounced crooked and was about to hit the edge. The coach chose a boy in red shorts and a girl in braids to be the first two bouncers. The two happy trampoliners climbed up onto the springy surface and began to bounce. Higher and higher they went as they gained confidence and soon it looked as if their heads would surely hit the rafters.

After everyone had a turn bouncing, the coach blew a whistle and several older students from the school gymnastics team came running in. First, a muscular boy climbed onto the trampoline, bounced several times until he was flying really high, and then did a series of flips in the air, always landing on his feet. Then a blond girl climbed up and began to bounce on her back and then on her belly, switching positions in the air as the younger children clapped and cheered. They could hardly wait until they could perform like that.

1. What color did you picture for the first boy's clothes?
2. What color do you picture for the hair of the last girl to bounce?
3. Why do you think the coach had the inexperienced jumpers go first?
4. Does it sound like safety rules are necessary for a trampoline? Why?
5. Why was it important to learn to bounce very high before learning to flip in the air?
6. Do you think it was important to learn how to control your jumping before learning tricks? Why?
7. Title!

The wasp and all his numerous family

I look upon as a major calamity.

He throws open his nest with prodigality,

But I distrust his waspitality.

-Ogden Nash

Level Eight

Level Eight

1.

The giraffe that lives on the plains of Africa is the tallest animal on earth. Making good use of its six-foot neck, it survives by eating the leaves of trees with its long black tongue reaching the highest branches. Its coloring, patterns and patches of yellow and brown, is perfect camouflage when standing in the shade of a tree, feeding. As might be expected, the giraffe has the highest blood pressure of any animal.

1. What is the main idea of this story?
2. What colors did you visualize for the giraffe's body?
3. Why do you think a giraffe needs camouflage?
4. Do you think being the tallest animal on earth keeps the giraffe safe from predators?
5. Why doesn't the giraffe just eat mostly grass like many other animals do?
6. How do you think a giraffe looks when it drinks water?
7. Why does a giraffe have the highest blood pressure of any animal?
8. What would happen to its brain if it didn't get blood to its head?
9. Do you think a giraffe would make a good pet? Why?

2.

In 1962, John Glenn was the first American to fly in orbit around the Earth. In a spacecraft called the Friendship 7, he circled the globe three times in just under five hours. When a space capsule re-enters the Earth's atmosphere from space, the outside of the craft becomes red hot. Just before John Glenn was due to splash down in the Atlantic Ocean after his last orbit, a signal told his ground crew that the heat shield on the spacecraft might be loose. There were some tense minutes when it was feared the shield would fail and Glenn and the spacecraft would burn up, but the shield held, and John Glenn returned to a hero's welcome.

1. What color do you think John Glenn saw the Earth?
2. Why do you think the Earth is primarily that color?
3. Why do you think the space craft needed a heat shield to protect it?
4. Why was being able to successfully orbit the Earth such an important part of space exploration?
5. What do you think happened first to John Glenn when he returned?
6. What do you think happened next to him?
7. Why do you think the United States space program wanted Glenn and this successful mission to get lots of public attention?

3.

Next to the elephant, the hippopotamus, weighing up to 8,000 pounds, is the largest land mammal. The huge vegetarian beast is found in or near the rivers and lakes of Africa. The animal is clumsy on land but very graceful in water. It can swim well and sometimes actually runs along the bottom. Since glands in the hippo's skin secrete a pinkish mucus, people used to think that hippopotamuses sweat blood.

    1. What numbers did you visualize that let you remember the exact weight of the hippopotamus?
    2. What did you visualize the hippo eating?
    3. Do you think it is probably best that the hippo is a vegetarian?
    4. How much food do you think a hippo eats?
    5. Why do you think a hippo is clumsy on land but nimble in the water?
    6. Main idea and title, please!

4.

Africa is home to some of the most diverse life forms on Earth, including both the tallest and shortest groups of people in the world. Pygmies, who reside in the jungle forests of central Africa, are rarely taller than four feet, eight inches. Pygmies live in bands of twenty or more and move about the forest erecting temporary camps. They build huts of saplings thatched with leaves. Pygmies hunt, fish, collect wild plant food, and trade with nearby farmers. The Watusi, cattle traders who inhabit the grasslands of central Africa, are a huge people, often being seven feet or taller.

    1. Where did you picture the Pygmies living?
    2. How tall did you picture the Pygmies being on average?
    3. What do you think the Pygmies do to generate their necessary food and materials?
    4. Why do you think the Pygmies live in bands of twenty or more?
    5. How tall do you picture the Watusi being, on the average?
    6. What kinds of jobs might the Pygmies or Watusi be best suited for in this country?

Level Eight

5. five sentences

It took the astronaut half an hour to get into his big cumbersome space suit. It looked like he had big white pillows strapped around him. The other astronauts in the space station, who were not in space suits, spun him around and held him upside down (which really doesn't mean much when you are weightless) and otherwise tormented him. To get away, the astronaut finally opened a hatch and floated outside into space where the others could not follow, connected to the ship by his oxygen hose. That is the real way the first "space walk" happened!

1. What does the astronaut's space suit look like in your imagery?
2. What colors did you picture in this story?
3. Why do you think it took the astronaut so long to get into his space suit?
4. What kinds of things do you think the other astronauts could do to "torment" him?
5. Do you think this was really the way the first space walk happened?
6. Why do you think this was called a "space walk"?
7. Main idea, please!

6. five sentences

Chameleons, lizards that mainly eat insects, capture food with their long tongues. Their gummy sticky tongues can be longer than their bodies, and are shot out to snare prey. Some larger chameleons eat birds and small rodents. Chameleons, whose basic color is green, can change color in response to heat, light, noise, or other influences. Contrary to many people's ideas, though, the range of color a chameleon can adopt is limited to shades of yellow, green, or brown.

1. What does the chameleon's tongue look like in your picture?
2. What do you picture for the way the chameleons "snare" their prey?
3. Why do you think chameleons can change color?
4. Why do you think the chameleons are limited to three colors?
5. Main idea?

7.

John Wesley Powell was one of the first white men to explore the canyon country of the American southwest. In 1869, he led a twelve-man expedition that traversed the Grand Canyon. They traveled in heavy wooden boats down the Colorado River through the heart of the canyon. At some places, they had to do "portage," or carry the boats around sections of the river that were too dangerous to float down. John Wesley Powell surveyed and mapped the river canyon for the government. What made Powell's feats amazing is that, as a result of a Civil War injury, he did it all with only one arm.

1. How many men did you visualize on Powell's expedition into the Grand Canyon?
2. What movement did you visualize in this story?
3. How many boats do you think they needed?
4. How do you think "heavy wooden boats" may have helped or hindered Powell's expedition?
5. Now we use rubber rafts to go down the Colorado River. In what ways can you visualize these being better or worse than the boats Powell used?
6. Why do you think the story said it was amazing that Powell did all of this exploration with only one arm?
7. What might you infer about Powell's good arm?
8. A good title, please!

8.

The first manned mission to the moon touched down on the lunar surface on July 20, 1969. One astronaut orbited the moon in the mother ship, the Columbia, while two other astronauts flew to the lunar surface in the Lunar Module Eagle. On the moon, the two astronauts erected the American flag and set up some scientific experiments. Then they took photographs and collected rock samples. When they were done, they hopped back into the Eagle, flew back to the Columbia, fired the larger spacecraft up, and headed for home. Four days later, they splashed down in the Pacific Ocean, safe and sound, and full of exciting new information from one of the most intriguing explorations in history.

1. How many astronauts did you visualize all together, and how many on the moon?
2. What does the name "Lunar Module" make you visualize?
3. Why do you think they named the mother ship "Columbia"?
4. Why do you think they named the Lunar Module "Eagle"?
5. Do you think the American flag is still on the moon? Why?
6. Do you think the astronauts really "hopped" back into the Eagle? Why?
7. Why did the Columbia have to orbit around the moon while waiting for the astronauts to return?

Level Eight

9.

seven sentences

About ninety percent of all people are right-handed. This is because in humans, the left side of the brain is usually dominant. Strangely enough, the left side of the brain controls the right side of the body. A small number of people are ambidextrous— they can use either hand equally well. Ambidextrous people tend to use the same hand for certain tasks. They may throw a ball left-handed, but use a pencil right-handed. It is interesting that among professional baseball players there is almost an equal number of right and left-handers.

1. What percent of people are right-handed?
2. Why do you think the percentage of right-handed people is so high?
3. What do you think might happen in the brain to allow people to be ambidextrous?
4. Why do you think professional baseball has almost an equal number of right and left-handers?
5. Also in baseball, why do you think some batters are called "switch-hitters"?
6. What might be true about the athletic abilities of left-handed people?
7. Do you think that left-handers are hindered in our culture? Why?
8. Main idea?

10.

eight sentences

The first known library, found in Iraq, held 30,000 clay tablets. They were inscribed with 7th century B.C. laws, business dealings, poetry, and news. A few hundred years later, the Pharaoh of Egypt had amassed a library of half a million papyrus scrolls. In China, the first library was created when one copy of every book in the land was put in the Emperor's library. All other copies were burned. The libraries in Europe in the Middle Ages were found in monasteries where manuscripts were slowly hand copied on parchment by the monks. The invention of the printing press lowered the cost of books and the number of libraries grew. Soon they began to resemble our libraries of today.

1. How many clay tablets were in the first known library?
2. How do you think the writing got on the clay tablets?
3. With 30,000 clay tablets, what might you guess about the physical attributes of the librarian?
4. What four things do you picture being inscribed on the tablets?
5. Why do you think all other copies of China's books were burned?
6. Besides lowering costs of books, what else do you think the printing press caused?
7. As books became cheaper, what do you think started happening among the people?
8. Title?

11.

Before the harnessing of electricity, people used a variety of different ways, including the use of smoke signals, for signaling over long distances. To signal with smoke, a really hot fire was first built. Then green leaves, or wet leaves, were thrown on the fire and allowed to smolder. The signaler then placed a blanket or animal skin on the smoldering fire to stop the smoke from rising. In a few seconds, the covering was removed and a large puff of white smoke would rise by itself into the sky. The size and shape of the smoke puffs could be controlled and used as a code that would be seen for miles.

Another early way of signaling was by pounding out different rhythms on big drums or even hollow logs. The loud booming sounds could be heard for several miles with different types of drumming meaning different things. Sometimes a kind of relay was used with drummers spread out in a line, a few miles apart, who would listen to the message of the drums and then repeat it. In this way, messages could travel fifty or even 100 miles in just a few minutes.

Wigwag, a system of signaling using flags, was invented during the American Civil War and used mostly between ships at sea. A signal man holding two brightly colored flags would wave them in a particular pattern that another signal man within eyesight could read. That signal man could then turn and relay the signal to another signal man farther along. This system was as fast or faster than drumming but with a few disadvantages. Wigwag would not work at night, it would not work in the fog, and it would not work if a ship sailed between two ships that were signaling each other and blocked their view.

1. What color did you picture for the smoke signals?
2. What did you picture for the colors and movements of wigwag signal flags?
3. What movement did you picture for what a smoke signaler does to make a puff?
4. What kinds of things would stop smoke signals from being an effective way to signal?
5. Which of the three methods of signaling do you think is best? Why?
6. Do you think any of these methods are used today?
7. What might help wigwag signaling from ship to ship work at night?
8. What is the main idea of this story?

Level Eight

12.

Robert opened the squeaky avocado-colored refrigerator and got some celery out of the crisper drawer. One by one, he broke off all the large, pale green stalks and washed them carefully in the sink. Then he cut the big whitish bottom ends, and also the small leafy top ends off the stalks. Next, he took each large, trimmed stalk and cut it into three equal lengths. When he was finished, he had almost two dozen four-inch pieces of celery.

Next, Robert got out peanut butter, spreadable cheese, and some cream cheese, and left them on the counter while he watched a TV show. When he returned to the kitchen everything had warmed to room temperature and was nice and soft. Robert spread one-third of the celery with brown chunky peanut butter, and another third with the bright orange cheese. Then he mixed chopped, spicy, green chives into the cream cheese, spread it on the remaining celery, and arranged everything on a large platter.

Robert looked happily at the clock—and then jumped a foot! Somehow it was now six-thirty, the party started at seven, and he still needed to clean up the kitchen and himself. He forced himself not to panic as he fed the chopped off celery tops and bottoms down the howling garbage disposal. Then he jammed the jars and bottles willy-nilly into the refrigerator and ran down the hall to the bathroom. Just combing his hair when the first guest rang the doorbell, he smoothly balanced the platter of hors d'oeuvres on one hand and headed for the door.

1. What colors did you picture for the stuff Robert was putting on the celery?
2. Why did Robert have to leave the celery stuffing out before he could spread it?
3. Where do you think the stuffing was kept, in a cupboard or refrigerator? Why?
4. What do you think "willy-nilly" means?
5. Do you think Robert had made this snack tray before? Why?
6. Title and main idea?